Gg Hh Ii Jj Kk Ll Mm

Uu Vv Ww Xx Yy Zz

Dear Parent,

The My First Steps to Reading® series is based on a teaching activity that helps children learn to recognize letters and their sounds. The use of predictable language patterns and repetition of familiar words will also help your child build a basic sight vocabulary. Your child will enjoy watching the characters in the books place imaginative objects in "letter boxes." You and your child can even create and fill your own letter box, using stuffed animals, cut-out pictures, or other objects beginning with the same letter. The things you can do together are limited only by your imagination. Learning letters will be fun—the first important step on the road to reading.

The Editors

My "d" Book

(Blends are included in this book.)

written by Jane Belk Moncure
illustrated by Colin King

Little  had a box.

"I will find things that begin
with my 'd' sound," she said.

"I will put them into my sound  box."

Little  found dolls.

She found all kinds of dolls,

dolls, and more dolls!

One doll danced.

One doll played a drum.

Did Little  put the dolls into her box? She did.

But some dolls fell out.

So Little  said,

"I will turn this box into
a house for the dolls!"

And she did.

Little  d made the dolls a

 desk

and a chest of  drawers.

14

She made a dining room with a table

and dishes  for the table.

Little

made the dolls some dresses.

She made all kinds of dresses.

Then she dressed her dolls . . .

and took them for a drive in the desert.

They saw a dromedary.

Little 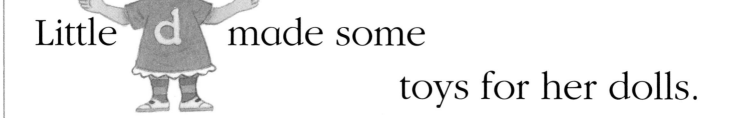 made some

toys for her dolls.

She made ducks

for her dolls.

She made dogs for her dolls.

She put the ducks and the dogs
into the house.

One day, a doll was sick.

So she took the doll to a doctor.

One day, a doll had a toothache.

So Little  took the doll

to a

dentist.

One day, Little walked out of her door.

"I will buy doughnuts for my dolls," she said.

"We will have doughnuts for dinner."

She put a dozen doughnuts on the dining room table.

doughnuts

dolls

dog

Why did she need a dozen?

dromedary

dolls' dresses

chest of
drawers

desk

ducks

Can you read these words with Little  ?

diamond

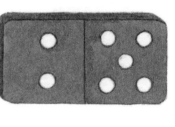
domino

diary

daisy

deer

dustpan

dove

dwarf

donkey

dandelion

dog

dinosaur

Aa Bb Cc Dd Ee Ff

Nn Oo Pp Qq Rr Ss Tt

My First
Steps to
READING®